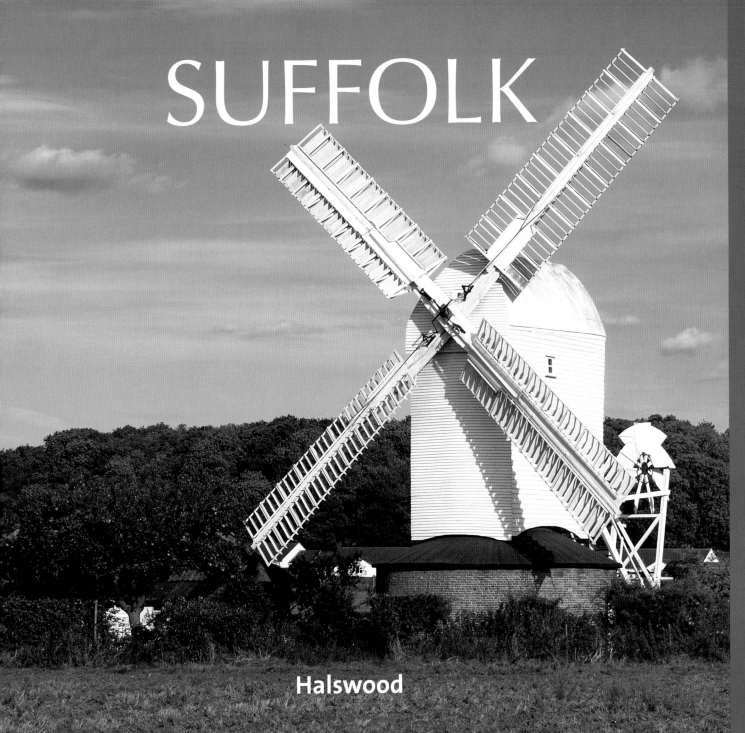

SUFFOLK

ADDRESS BOOK

Halswood

Published by Halswood Stationers

Copyright © Halswood Stationers
Image copyright © Mark Staples

British Library Cataloguing-in-Publication Data
A CIP record for this title is available from the
British Library

ISBN 978 0 85717 019 4

HALSWOOD STATIONERS
Halsgrove House,
Ryelands Industrial Estate,
Bagley Road, Wellington, Somerset TA21 9PZ
Tel: 01823 653777   Fax: 01823 216796
email: sales@halsgrove.com

Part of the Halsgrove group of companies
Information on all Halsgrove titles is available at:
www.halsgrove.com

Printed and bound in China by
Toppan Leefung Printing Ltd (0)

Front cover: Beach huts, Southwold.

Back cover: Herringfleet Smock Mill.

Title page: Stanton Post Mill has been fully restored
and still produces flour on a regular basis.

Overleaf: Thatched cottages in the village of Kersey.

Built between 1165 and 1173 by Henry II, all that
remains of Orford Castle today is its Great Tower.

YOUR ADDRESS BOOK

Since the invention of the camera in the mid nineteenth century, photographers have found much to inspire them in the Suffolk landscape. Today, with digital cameras so widely available, almost everyone has an opportunity to capture mementos of a favourite place, or a chance event. But not all of us have the skill, or patience, to wait for that single moment when all the conditions fall into place and the perfect image is captured.

Mark Staples, whose photographs appear in this book moved to Suffolk fifteen years ago as a newly qualified teacher of Modern Languages and has remained ever since. His interest in photography began on seeing some photographs taken by friends using a simple digital compact. Inspired by these images and having enjoyed drawing and painting as a youngster, Mark decided to pursue this newly discovered interest in digital photography, and couple it with his other love of travel.

Suffolk remains one of the most remote, attractive and unspoilt counties in England, as the photographs included here amply portray. While its largest towns have all the vibrancy of modern life, much of the county is rural, retaining its character founded in earlier times: pretty villages with timbered and brick-built cottages, and isolated farms as they have endured for centuries, set solidly in the rolling landscape. It is a county that is imbued with history at every turn. From the picturesque coast to striking inland vistas, and from impressive townscapes to tiny hamlets, Mark has been able to find a scene or scenery to arrest our interest. To see more of Mark's photos, visit his website: www.markstaples.co.uk

Address books tend to be well used and have a long life. Along with important contact details, they keep track of the user's friends and acquaintances, tracing their lives over time and from place to place. And, if properly attended to, an address book eventually becomes a journal in itself, and an attractive and permanent keepsake.

Whether you have bought this book for your own use, or receive it as a gift, we hope this *Suffolk Address Book,* with its superb pictorial reminders of Suffolk, provides years of pleasure.

USEFUL ADDRESSES AND TELEPHONE NUMBERS

A

Beach huts, Southwold.

A

Holy Trinity Church, in the village of Long Melford.

B

A pretty cottage in the village of Ufford, near Woodbridge.

B

B

B

Aldeburgh seafront houses add a splash of colour against the shingle.

C

Kersey ford. The village is famed for its Kersey cloth.

C

C

C

D

Debenham Village Sign betrays its former wool-trade status.

D

D

D

Early autumn colours on the green in the little village of Hartest.

E

The Suffolk landscape at harvest time; Freston, near Ipswich.

E

E

E

On the Orwell at Pin Mill.

F

A Cavendish cottage painted in a variant of 'Suffolk pink.'

F

F

F

Walberswick, on the River Blyth.

G

Herringfleet Smock Mill lies in the village of
the same name on the River Waveney.

G

G

G

Modern beach huts at Lowestoft.

H

The pretty Moulton packhorse bridge on the old route
from Cambridge to Bury St Edmunds.

H

H

H

I

The village sign in Monks Eleigh.

I

The Victorian wet docks of Ipswich,
transformed by modern development.

A carpet of flowering heather on Dunwich Heath.

J

The Sole Bay Inn at the foot of the lighthouse in Southwold

K

The beautiful Abbey Gardens and Cathedral, Bury St Edmunds.

K

The Orwell Bridge carries the A14 across the River Orwell.

L

The pier, Southwold.

L

L

L

Swans at Thorpeness Meare boating lake.

M

Pakenham near Bury St Edmunds.

M

M

M

Stoke-By-Nayland lies on the Suffolk-Essex border in Constable country.

Maggi Hambling's 'Scallop' stands on the beach between Aldeburgh and Thorpeness. The sculpture commemorates the life of composer Benjamin Britten.

N

The Old Custom House, Ipswich, was constructed in 1845.

O

C

Sailing on Oulton Broad.

O

Ipswich Waterfront at night.

Springtime in the village of Chelsworth.

PQ

The golden sands of the Southwold beach.

R

Striking thatched cottages in Somerleyton.

R

A magnificent example of one of the numerous timber-framed buildings in the medieval town of Lavenham.

Lowestoft Haven Marina.

S

S

S

Coastguard cottages at Shingle Street.

The River Deben at Woodbridge.

T

The freshly colour-washed Little Hall stands
on the main square in Lavenham.

The walled garden at Helmingham Hall.

UV

The Ramsholt Arms overlooking the River Deben.

The House in the Clouds at Thorpeness was
converted from an old water tower.

W

The historic Thames barge *Cygnet of Harwich*
pictured on the River Alde in Snape

Autumn in the Abbey Gardens, Bury St Edmunds.

XYZ